JOURNAL

Covenant®

Printed in Canada on Acid Free Paper